CHOOSE YOUR WEAPON

CONTENTS:

D0111559

HAMBURG // LONDON // LOS ANGELES // TOKYO

Choose Your Weapon Sampler Vol 1

Graphic Design - Jason Milligan
Layout – Erika Terriquez
Project Coordinators – Jonathan Chen and Rob Tokar

Digital Imaging Manager - Chris Buford
Pre-Production Supervisor - Erika Terriquez
Art Director - Anne Marie Horne
Production Manager - Elisabeth Brizzi
Managing Editor - Vy Nguyen
VP of Production - Ron Klamert
Editor-in-Chief - Rob Tokar
Publisher - Mike Kiley
President and C.O.O. - John Parker
C.E.O. and Chief Creative Officer - Stuart Levy

A **TOKYOPOP** Manga

TOKYOPOP and ☜ are trademarks or registered trademarks of TOKYOPOP Inc.

TOKYOPOP Inc.
5900 Wilshire Blvd. Suite 2000
Los Angeles, CA 90036

E-mail: info@TOKYOPOP.com
Come visit us online at www.TOKYOPOP.com

ISBN: 978-1-4278-0234-7

First TOKYOPOP printing: February 2007
10 9 8 7 6 5 4 3 2 1
Printed in the USA

Dulan, Year 517

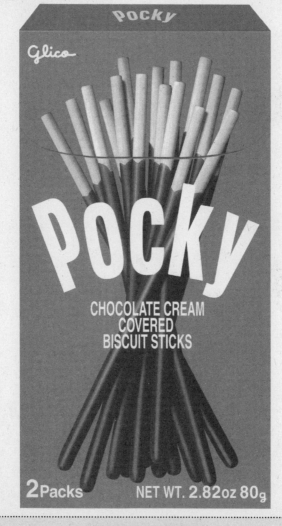

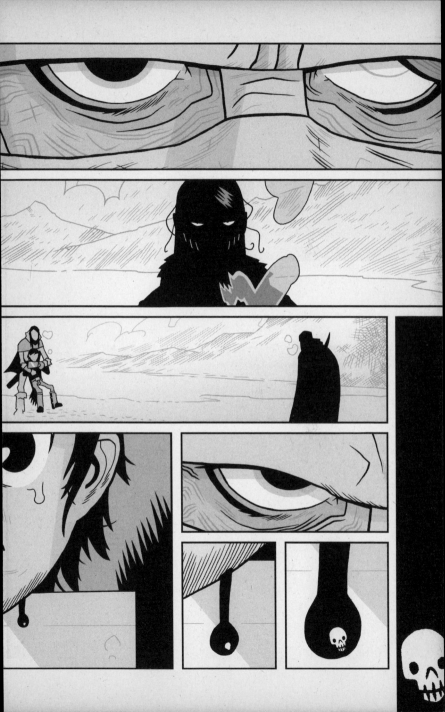

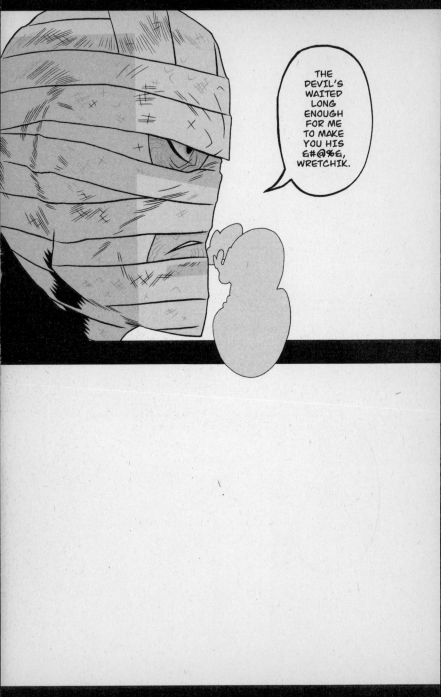

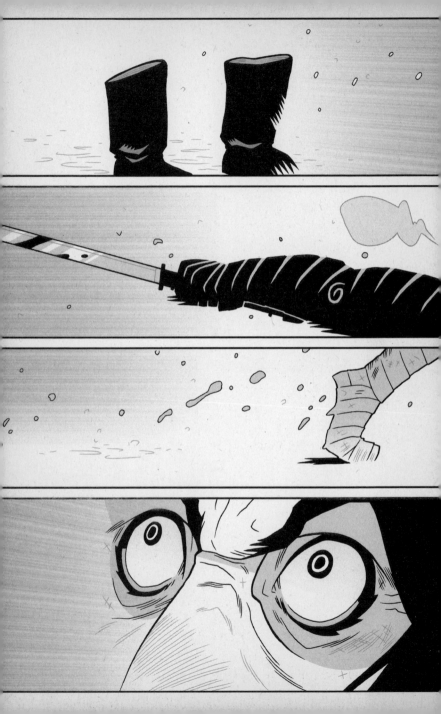

PERHAPS **NOW** WOULD BE AN APPROPRIATE TIME TO WARN YOU: THIS WILL **NOT** END WELL.

IF YOU ARE HERE FOR A HAPPY TALE, A TALE OF **LOVE** AND **JOY**, LOOK ELSEWHERE.

THAT IS NOT TO SAY THAT LOVE AND JOY HAVE NO PART IN THIS TALE. I SUPPOSE IT IS IN THE NATURE OF EVEN THE **DARKEST** PLOT TO DANGLE SUCH THINGS BEFORE YOU, IF BUT TO **MISLEAD**.

AND IN ALL CANDOR, I FEAR THAT INDEED I ALREADY **HAVE**, SO EARLY IN THE TELLING.

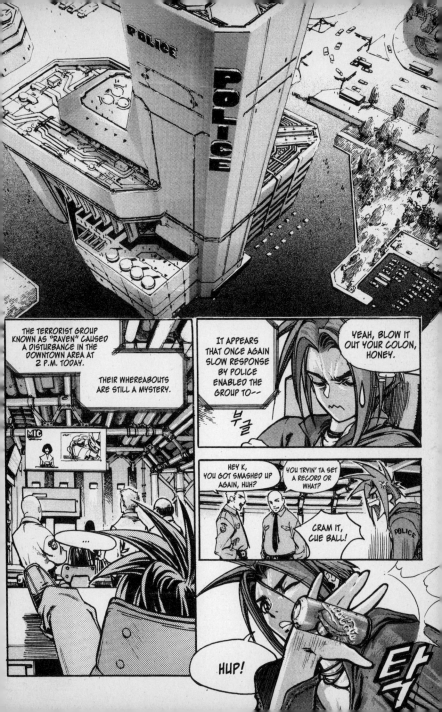

...THEY NEVER REVEAL THEIR SOURCES FOR THAT INTEL.

TAKE WHAT JUST HAPPENED WITH YOU. IT WOULD'VE BEEN EASIER FOR THEM IF THEY HAD JUST SHOT THE COCKPIT RATHER THAN THE ARM.

BUT THEY DIDN'T DO THAT.

AND IT'S NOT LIKE WE'VE EVER SEEN THESE "PLOTS" FOR OURSELVES.

MNC: Multi-National Corporation

I WONDER IF THE TRUTH ABOUT THIS CITY IS AS CUT AND DRIED AS THEY LEAD US TO BELIEVE...

IF THEY REALLY ARE TERRORISTS, THEN WHY GO THE LESS LETHAL, MORE TROUBLESOME ROUTE?

I DUNNO, K...SOMETIMES WHEN I JUST SIT DOWN AND REALLY THINK ABOUT IT...I JUST WONDER, IS ALL.

YURA, WHAT ARE YOU TALKING ABOUT?

MAYBE I COULD FLY STRAIGHTER IF I HAD A MECH WITH A FACTORY DATE THAT WASN'T BEFORE I WAS BORN!

I'M SO SICK OF THESE RATTY TCs OF OURS!

CHIEF--EVEN THE CORPORATE SECURITY CLEANERS ARE NEWER THAN OUR MECHS!

THEY CAN *AFFORD* THEM!

A COP'S EQUIPMENT SHOULDN'T BE INFERIOR TO A CIVILIAN'S!

Cleaners: MNC private mech armies

IT'S YOUR JOB AS A POLICEMAN TO MAKE IT WORK!

You salary thief, you!

JERK.

AND ARE YOU GOING TO PAY FOR A NEW ONE?!

SPEAKING OF... WHAT'S UP WITH THAT FEELING I GOT DURING THE FIGHT TODAY?

COULD IT BE...

...THAT I'M A NEWTYPE?!

IT WAS LIKE... I COULD READ MY OPPONENT'S MIND...

Newtype: Genetically engineered superhumans who have extrasensory abilities (at least according to *Gundam*)

TRY THIS ON FOR SIZE.

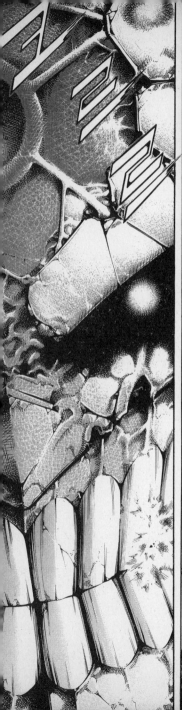